GW00646637

THE QUIET PART LOUD

THE QUIET PART LOUD

Stories

Tyler Barton

The Quiet Part Loud © 2018, Tyler Barton. All rights reserved. No part of this book may be used or reproduced without consent from the author or publisher except in the case of brief quotations appropriated for use in articles and reviews.

Published by Split/Lip Press
6710 S. 87th St.
Ralston, NE 68127
www.splitlippress.com

ISBN: 978-1952897023

Cover Art by Jayme Cawthern
Cover Art images by Rebecca Fish Ewan

TABLE OF CONTENTS

It hasn't happened yet.
It hasn't begun or ended.
It hasn't granted us its bliss
or exploded in our faces.

—Laura Kasischke, "They say"

Stay, Go

In Jersey, we did neither.

My boyfriend and I just rode the elevator. At the Hampton all weekend, we pranked guests, conducted social experiments, collected data we never wrote down. Facing the wall, backs to the elevator doors, we challenged anyone to join us in our error. Our metrics: how many people would turn to stand like us? How long until they flipped? How many seconds until everyone in the elevator stood backward like us runaways? Most turned immediately. We hid our faces. If the audience asked questions, we kept silent. That's what Marco called everyone else but me: audience. Only once did someone try to correct us—an outlier, meaningless, but I remember her French tips, zebra-stripes, the knock her stilettos made on the marble. *Son,* she whispered, *turn around.* I pulled a glossy paper bird from my pocket, handed it to her, and said *Shhhhh.*

What waited in our room was a big bleach stain on the carpet—a mistake in my makeover, and it stank. Marco pinched me some glasses from the hotel bar and my disguise was complete. Now I was a man—astute, escaped, sixteen, free, my blond hair leaning a little green—who looked nothing like the photo of the boy on the news. They said I'd been missing for two days, but we didn't like that term. Missing. Was there a word for somewhere between *lost* and *found?*

We never left the Hampton. We camped in the elevator, where we could feel what the streets of Newark offered, but feeling was enough—the long breath of possibility, a little fear, a little hope, even that faint, foul scent of crab. We held on to that. We lingered. If we hung out in the room at all it was for sex, or showers, or we passed time coloring each other's hair and folding the pages of porn into origami. These were skills I believed, somehow, someday, might come in handy—patience, focus, how to see a line before it's there. I made animals; Marco, aircrafts. I loved him. He had dark, wide, stubborn hair I could pin down into braids and dye individually. His dreads looked like Nerds Rope. Nights, I toyed with those cords until he slept and then penned muddled, unsendable letters to my mother on hotel stationery.

Marco's favorite act—we called it *The No You*—was where we'd stand as close as possible to the doors, a few other passengers behind us, and wait for the elevator to open on the lobby. Then, one of us would motion for the other to go first. *No, you,* the other would say.

> *Oh, but I insist.*

> *You're so polite, but seriously, it's all you.*

No, you.

You.

You!

Eventually the people waiting behind us would angle their way out, hurrying past before the doors trapped everyone in. We kept a timer. The record was set when the doors closed and not a single person had left. Together we rode right back up—all of us.

I laughed so hard Marco had to hold me.

We never agreed on much, but we were firm in our belief that the true draw of a hotel was its elevator. Tight space, dim light, the lottery of who will join that awkward, heavy quiet. The elevator is the trip. The elevator means you're almost there. It's almost sex, almost dinner, almost show, museum, zoo, almost sleeping spread wide as a starfish. Almost a scalding shower, almost a cab ride. In an elevator there's not much to do except be alive around each other. Most just look at their shoes, or their phones (we'd ditched ours for fear of tracking), or those glowing buttons. If you're brave you can look at other people's faces—you're allowed—but no one does. If you're us, you can hand them a horse folded out of porn. We were romantic in that way, in our need to unseam social norms. We were whispering our message: the whole essence of travel is distilled into middle spaces. Empty moments. Though common knowledge says an elevator is for people with a place to go, we said no. We rode over and over and over.

Our place to be right now was here.

Marco had come into some money the day he turned eighteen, two weeks earlier, something about a second uncle who had, for a brief and litigious time, been mayor of the city of Orlando. We didn't know what we were doing in Newark, or anywhere. We were working through it at the Hampton. Sometimes we ordered room service cocktails, but we never went into bars to use our fake IDs. By Sunday, it'd been three days at that hotel. We sat on the window-side loveseat in our room like, *Okay, let's figure this out:* we can go north. A ton of cheap land in Maine. We could try Canada, where health insurance is a right. We could go home and kill our parents, haha. But for Marco, that meant central Florida, where his Mom lived. He shook his head.

"Okay," I said. "Seriously, let's make a plan."

Marco laughed and flew his porno plane—smack—into the window.

The origami I obsessed over that weekend was this bird called a swallow. It's a bitch because you have to unfold the whole thing completely just to get a final crease in the beak. You spend half an hour crafting and then you have to take each piece apart to finish. My hands would shake like the hotel was coming down. *Chill out,* Marco would whine. *I'm really trying,* I'd say.

Instead of a plan, we spent Sunday afternoon devising new ruses. We returned to the elevator, dragging in a chair from our room. I wore a dress and sat with a magazine in my lap. When the box was full of people in severe heels, hairspray, and luminescent dresses, it began. Marco entered in a bathrobe fashioned as a lab-coat, holding a clipboard he'd nabbed from the front desk. He placed a hand on my shoulder and my whole body raced with anticipation. Then, he spoke with a deep, doctorly, bedside manner: "Ma'am, we have the results."

"Oh god," I sighed. "Give it to me straight." I forgot to mention I was wearing my Lady Gaga wig—white-blond with those goddess bangs—the one I used on the getaway drive from Pennsylvania. I'd taken to sleeping with it on, even though we'd cut and dyed my hair to hell.

Marco took a deep breath, put a hand on my shoulder, and said, "You're a homosexual."

Here I sobbed on cue.

That night I learned of my talent for crying on command. All I had to do was conjure up my mother's face thinking about my face. I bawled until the lenses of my glasses fogged.

Marco asked the passengers to pray for me. As the elevator doors pulled open, someone clapped, ruining everything. I threw the wig on the floor. We wanted to create discomfort, not entertainment. We didn't understand that they were the same thing.

I think that what Marco and I truly wanted was to be in that box when the machine got stuck between floors, to be trapped and not at fault for it, to have men in yellow uniforms pry open the doors and pull us to safety. At least—I think—that's what I wanted.

So, that night, we rode into morning. But something was off. Waking up in a Hampton on a Monday would feel, just, wrong. The hotel loses all its cachet if there's no next destination. How do you savor the middle if there is no end? You only crease the page because you know it will be a bird. Plus, honestly, how much of Marco's money were we going to spend on these games? We'd had three days to figure it out.

We paced the 8x8 box of the Hampton's elevator 3. No one else was getting on. The sun—you could see it from the eighteenth floor window each time the doors slid open—had begun to bubble above the skyline, and that's when a security guard walked into the elevator.

"I've heard about you two," he said. His uniform was too small and his tattoos showed.

Marco immediately began speaking in Spanish (*Vete, audiencia!*). I did some quasi-ASL, random gestures, eventually moving my fingers like scissors, pantomiming slicing off my ears.

"So you're artists," he said, ripping the wig from my head. "An artist worth $10,000 dollars." Then he had Marco by a braid. "An artist worth a long sentence for kidnapping a minor." The elevator stopped. The doors weren't opening. He killed his squawking radio.

Marco promised to dye the guard's hair any color he wanted. I offered an origami dog. Then a blowjob.

Marco laughed but looked at me sideways like, *How much of this is a joke?* My offer hung there in the air, and as the door parted open, the guard smiled.

Marco shoved him hard, and we flew, swooping into the dark city like bats.

Growing up I learned something I don't think most kids know, which is that the best part of a vacation is before it ever starts. That preceding day and a half when the thing feels finally here, when you're packing, singing, making plans for classmates to collect your worksheets—the restless sleep you take on the eve of the drive. Nothing, not even the first turn in the road, the first stop at Sunoco, the first rip in a bag of SunChips, nothing yet has ended. No one is screaming. Neither parent has had *Enough*. The single ticket flight back to Pennsylvania is still unbooked. A jellyfish has not yet stung you. A stranger is not pissing on your hand.

What I mean is the night before Marco came for me—sleeping in the backyard on the broken trampoline, the black vinyl bed sagging into the wet grass—was the best day of my life.

That restless sleep contained every part of the world.

I remember I woke to the rattling of springs, terrified.

After the guard, we switched hotels. The Marriott was no destination, but there we were, stuck in another interim space. These elevators had AC, colored lights, and the weirdest thing ever: doors on either side of the compartment. You'd reach a floor and have to guess which set would open. It unnerved me.

But then Marco discovered how, at the top floor, both doors opened at once. The new plan was to stand outside the elevator, and when those doors slid open: run, leap, clear the empty elevator completely. I tried to imagine us landing firm-footed in the opposite lobby.

We stood on the twenty-fourth story and waited for the bell to ding. For our path to open. For the double row of doors to unfold like a swallow.

And when they did, we saw straight through to the other side.

You, he said.

No, you, I mean it.

Hiccups Forever

An hour after it happened, I watched our house explode. Friday, in History. Evan's phone got passed around under the tables. I was the last to watch, dropped his phone, cracked the screen. Then the hiccups came. They haven't left. You can still watch the video on Youtube. It's there. Search "York County Home Disintegrates in Gas Explosion." A cop car parked on our block had a dashcam going. It's a normal day. Spring. Blue sky. Mr. Simms has Groucho on a walk. On the left, a white house goes pufferfish. For a millisecond it's still our house, just expanded, with space in between every piece. You can see sky through each tiny seam. My green room spreads out. Then: confetti. Black confetti. Our dog dies. Groucho barks. Mr. Simms runs past the camera. Nobody knew it was my house when they handed me the phone. They don't even know my name is Cara. I watched it anyway. I've watched it a lot. The video played on Facebook all weekend. People said it was awesome, which was weird. But I shared it too. Twenty-seven likes—a personal record. La Quinta's manager put my parents in separate rooms. The other guests couldn't sleep with all their loud blame. My sister Jenna told me, "Kiss everything normal bye," and "I can't sleep with you making those noises." So I've been lying on a booth in the hotel breakfast nook every night, wondering what she means and hiccupping. Nobody's sharing the video anymore, but I still watch it. A lot. On the computer in the lobby. Full-screened, reversed, dragging the button left across the page. Slow as possible. It's cool. Every piece has somewhere to go. Everything shrinks back together. My hiccups stop. It's weird. Played forward, the house-pieces float there until they disappear. That's the future, I think. What Jenna means. When I let go of the mouse, I hiccup. Eight seconds: our house is over. Even the smoke's gone. Just blue. Springtime. Groucho barking. Like we were never there. But watching in reverse, it's different. In reverse, I can breathe. Plus it's prettier, like a party when everyone finally shows up, before anybody starts to leave.

K,

1. On that Fishtown roof we laid down cardboard from the Papa John's dumpster and danced. Two b-boys, but you were better. The sun had just set, the sky all about that smoky purple light. I set the camcorder on the AC unit and framed you. Thumbs up. Your shirt off. Your face never not ready to be legendary, Wheaties box, movie poster. Elbows loose. Gravel shifting beneath the cardboard, so on six-steps it looked like we were skating, floating, still but still moving. We didn't even play a song, I just clapped, because Fuck it, we'd add the track later when something worthy dropped, the new Nas, who knows. This tape, your ticket, my street cred, that bandwagon, or at the very least our guaranteed, ready-made nostalgia like Holy shit Oh my god when we'd find the film decades later in a box after moving to the suburbs, our kids saying, "Daddy, what *is?*" What did we do? We were teenaged but we knew the tape was the thing, to have proof, to hold in your hands what you'd made. To be named. Like those all-city writers who bombed the maroon SEPTA trolley tour, foreigners gawking at all the thousand city murals like, Bitch you got one right out the window, just look at where your hand's hanging, haha. We could see them from the roof. We had a laugh. It was fun. It

was more than that, breaking. It was . . . what'd you always say about dance?

2. Then that night manager wanted us off the roof. We yelled down some dumb shit like we were allowed, legit. He sold pizzas. He had pimples. He—I can only see this now—was a kid just doing his job. But we hated his tone, his acne scars. We talked back in kicks, freezes, downrock, windmill, suicide, tossing our arms around like dirty jokes. And when the police showed, you grabbed the camera, needed just one lone frame of their red and blue lights blinking. A perfect resolution to our tape's story. Remember your mantra, that white tee you sharpied with softy letters? EVERY STORY IS A DANCE WITH NO BEGINNING. We were gonna sell that design. But the cop called us down. He said, "Now."

3. And he didn't help us. No, just called for backup and watched our asses climbing backwards down the gutter. When I touched the ground, I sprinted deep into the alley, but then he cornered you at the dumpster, threw you to the blacktop. Broken glass in your braids, remember later how I tried to pick it out, you slapped my hand away? We walked home over sidewalks in silence. You had the slightest limp. I didn't bring it up. I said Peace. You never said Peace.

4. My daughters asked me why I used to breakdance, which (thank God) is an easier one than *Why don't you still?* I remember I broke to stay sober, needed an addiction different than my dad's, but you, K, you danced for transportation. *Easiest way to leave a place is out the mind.* I remember you broke with your eyes closed. We put our energies into these tapes, these moves, crimes but victimless. We could b-boy anyplace—only climbed that roof for the view. As if anybody watching the tape would be able to look past you.

5. That night, the door to your aunt's building. You turned to me and made a face. You turned it inside out.

6. Our tape scared my girls. "Daddy's on a roof?" They'd seen a neighbor fall from one. Sits crooked in a wheelchair under the carport now. They giggle at him from our front yard but pray for him in church. You never did have the leg looked at, never watched the video either. Even though I called your aunt's house on the daily, asking you to come over, let's play the tape, and I had this application Mrs. Raines wanted me to give you for U Arts, but you swore: *They don't wanna let us dance there. They wanna choreograph us.* You always sounded right. But that was the problem, most times it was only the sound.

*

7. My girls, tonight, on the back patio—they're trying to be you. I'm grading papers. Kia's tucked in a ball on the concrete, and Becca's turning her in circles. Backspin. You knew that move. You still know that move. It's the last one on the tape before the sirens. I know that cop said shit to you, whispered in your ear, bent your arms back like an airflare, kicked your knee. You didn't do anything. I didn't do anything, standing back a hundred feet. We hadn't done anything. They didn't know what we were doing. We knew what we were doing. They kept looking around at the ground for dice. Motherfucking dice? A one hitter, baggies. Roaches. What's it matter? Then he looked right at your body. Stared at your sweat. Like a shirt the way it covered you. You did nothing. The sun's gone tonight. We're out of light.

8. And what have you done with yourself, with life, your body, the way it can move, freeze, break? With me. I found you online, your name listed in a short article. With mug shots. They got you. With a shotgun. Regardless of whoever did whatever it was. With the tape, in my old notebook, I found your email—bboykk@aim.com—but it bounced back. With gibberish. Now I'm writing on yellow paper. With a pen. Like the way I wrote my rhymes. Because my moves were weak I thought maybe I could rap. With fire. But you were right when you said I couldn't go even eight bars without lying. Like I did

just now: cus I don't know if you did what's in the paper. They frame you? Maybe. I don't know anything. Another lie: I don't know if you did shit with your life or not, cus I left, stopped visiting, and you used to call me at my job, after my night classes, the phone blinking red beside the register out at that West Chester Wawa, your dumb drunk crank calls, how I always hung up. With violence.

9. Kia asks why Mommy's the only one with friends. I gotta chat politics and basketball with their husbands. I don't know the rules to basketball. What color's a fucking basketball? One time back in college, when she was just my girl, she asked me to list all the people I'd kissed. I laughed, I don't know. "You seem upset," she said.

10. All that mattered was letting it go. But Mrs. Raines— remember her History class?—she knew too. Said all that matters is being true.

11. Remember picking our b-boy names from a thesaurus? Sharpies on our arms, you did mine, I did yours. I remember cutting the sleeves off your orange windbreaker. Trendsetter. Vanguard. I've never seen another body move like yours. Did we call that night manager *faggot*? We were laughing, but did I threaten his life? Did he ask what we were doing on the roof?

Was he just curious? Why were we afraid? Was it for no reason? Why did you stay? Some kind of statement nobody could decode? Did that squad car follow us home? Did it follow you alone?

12. My wife owns every season of *So You Think You Can Dance* on DVD. Calls it comfort food. I did a shitty 2000 at our wedding, turning on my hands like a top. She pop-locked. I wish you'd been there. Ripped a tear right through my jacket. Fucking breaking in a tux. You believe this? You were the better dancer. But you needed me next to you for proof. Beside me you shined. Your fingers were callused but still soft as communion bread. I'm drunk off wine. In the motherfucking suburbs. And almost out of paper.

-B

Fuck.

I was gonna leave it at a twelve-bar, let the beat rock through the last four, but I forgot about the video, the whole reason I'm writing . . .

. . . forget your sweaty braids whipping like branches in a storm, white kicks scuffed grey and brown, the fact that the camera wasn't even focused on us, or ours. Think only of your two legs and an arm held stiff in the air, making the shape of your first initial—K. I made this four-second clip, K. If we'd had more time, K, if the cop call hadn't gotten through, if the pimpled kid wasn't scared, K, if police couldn't speed, if I hadn't run away, K, you would keep dancing through every letter. Until the whole city knew your name. It plays over and over on my desktop. The girls clap every time it's done. K. They're never not clapping for you, for you to finish the sentence.

Whatever's the Worst that Could Happen We Want

Neither of us was a botanist, but breaking into the greenhouse was easy. And the wide booths at Chipotle made fondling possible. And the lounge in the basement of the Student Memorial Center was always empty.

"You're like, always having sex," our friends would say, the five of us standing in line at Film Club's midnight showings, or half-listening to washed-up comics in Steinman Theatre. The joke went: we were having sex in class, even when we were in separate classes. We could just think about each other and be fucking.

Her theory, which was my theory because this was college at nineteen, said that recklessness delivered joy, joy, joy, and eventually some kind of barrel-bottom. The beautiful way she explained it: you wanted that bottom—and then, you look up.

"The way you look up at me when I'm on top," she explained, which made sense, the way possibilities only seemed perfectly endless from the lowest vantage point. On me she would grind, as I tried to open my already open eyes. The leaves big as boogie boards, the flowers five-colored and wet. A concrete floor, but the beds were dirt soft. We sunk in. We ruined student science in the name of knocking down our lives, so sure that we couldn't wait to start all over.

Late-Teens on Trash Night

Trash night was instinct. Trash night was ours. Trash night with nothing we knew we owned. Trash night because. Fuck a sun. Trash night.

Twice a year every rule about what you could toss out was tossed out and all the homes in York County threw away what, in the past six months, had become junk to them. Mountains at the end of every driveway. What we had between us were four urgent boredoms, one license, and a Buick Century station wagon.

      Trash night meant ten discarded traffic cones we'd arranged to snake down Old Well Hill, and trash night was trying to mow them all over in a single pass, and trash night was the elusive nature of success. One would always jam up in the wheel well and veer us. We wanted to hit all the things you couldn't, on normal nights, even touch. Like this set of six windows, rotted in their frames, stacked against the trash tote at 42 Briar Lane. Dan hopped out first and put his boot through one. "Chill, man!" Harvey said, while Barkley slept in the way-backseat. In the street, I propped up another window with rocks and took the Buick into it.

It was my father's car but all the stickers on it belonged to me.

"Next stash," Harvey said. "Lemme look through it before we smash anything? Okay?"

Trigger-happy, Dan punched my rearview mirror— "Sounds like you don't understand trash night!"

"It's just, dude," Harvey said. "I need Christmas presents."

"Santa Claus over here," Dan said, drumming hard on my dash, trying to hit the rumored sweet spot that would activate the airbag. Dan was short, his sense of humor low-rent but pure. His Brooklyn accent made no sense here beside the Mason-Dixon line. This thing he wanted so bad never happened, but I'll never forget it, and if I ever run into him, say at a truck stop bar, I'll cock back and pop him in the mouth, because his dream was to out of the blue have his shoulder tapped and turn his head right into a big swing of fist. He wanted to be punched square and sudden, with no clue it was coming. Often he'd announce this, around a campfire or diner booth, and we'd laugh, saying, "Okay, man," but he'd make us swear to hold off until he'd forgotten ever asking to be hurt.

No tunes on trash night. My friends and me, we listened to the wind, the different notes hit when certain windows were a certain level of open. Barkley, the runt of our bunch, would freeze in that backward-facing bench seat, doing his solemn duty, which was to peer out the rear window for a last look at any trash we might have missed.

I remember it was 4:00 AM, because that was my father's wake-up time. Barkley said in his thin lisp: *stop, stop, go back*—and twenty miles away in the laundry closet adjacent to my basement bedroom, my dad was dressing in yesterday's greasy jeans for work. Some nights, nights that weren't trash night, I'd wake up and glimpse his pale, pocked ass in the moonlight and know with total confidence that adulthood was a fucked-up curse.

Barkley's pleas got louder, and I listened. The Buick's brake stopped us. It wouldn't always. I reversed down the farm road, doing twenty-five around the bend like a stuntman, Dan cheering, Barkley screaming "Trash night!" meaning: *stop here.*

It was a farmhouse with a long stone driveway. Among their junk a whole cabinet stood up in the dark. The moon viewed us opening drawers, and the moon didn't care about Harvey's dream of a garbage gift for his sister's Christmas, but the moon still laughed at us, not with.

We inspected the stash because even though the sky was brightening, it was trash night. Plus the sun was still buried somewhere behind Blue Mountain, so Barkley bent down to pick up what he'd seen from the back seat—a squat, silver vase, shut tight with a black lid—and Dan ripped it out of his hands, cocking back to whip it at the family's mailbox.

"Hey, hey, hey, hey," Harvey intervened. "Hey, dude. Thank you. Jesus."

The top came off with a pop and we all tried to look down in, but our only light, the moon, was blocked by our heads, which all knocked together. We squinted. The rods in the back of our eyes threw everything they had at it. We were speechless, because each of us, for a moment, knew the exact same thing.

"That's ashes," said Dan. "Somebody's damn dad is in that pot."

"Urn," I said, and I think it might've been my first time. So I said it again. Urn.

"Urn," Harvey said. *Urn*, Barkley too. And for a whole minute the four of us just put our hands on the thing and incanted the word—*Urn, Urn*. We sounded like animals in mourning. Naturally, Dan turned it into a game of Penis where you take turns saying a vulgar word louder and louder until someone gets chicken and refuses to yell again. Dan always won Penis. When he arched his back and howled it—*Urn!*—a porch light ignited. A hand pulled back the curtain.

Running is the mood I remember most from my teen years. Running in the dark. Running in the dark is an ethos. Trash night, pathos. I don't remember, ever, any logic with us.

Barkley buckled the urn into the seat beside him.

"Who would give away a body?"

"A bunch of ashes ain't a body."

"It's not nothing."

I didn't know who was talking anymore—my ears were ringing. I tried to turn the high beams on a higher setting, but blue, sudsy windshield juice kept streaking up across our view.

"Whatever, dude. This whole thing, it's just very un-trash night."

"But it's not trash night anymore," someone said, as we all stared through the window, the gold skull of the sun unburying itself from the mountain.

Models

The girl whose father shot her mother and then himself, she sat across from me in homeroom. Every morning I shivered through the pledge in Mrs. Cage's class, staring at Alexis Cashman's empty seat, selfish and stupid, wondering exactly how much school you get to miss if your dad loses it that bad.

This was Pennsylvania, early spring in the mid-aughts. Silver mornings with steady breezes blasting the paper mill's ass-breath through the single stoplight of Deliver borough. During the short crosstown walk from mom's apartment to Deliver High, the sun could never make its way above the hills we called mountains.

Distant is who I wanted to be, but failed, in my new camo crewneck it turned out three other juniors had also found at Walmart. Blonde metalhead hair frizzed out to my shoulders, just short of hiding the cords of my earbuds. Cool, removed, in it but not of it, a step back, cracking jokes, smiling only if you mistook my sneer—yet there I was, fixed on Lex's absence. That empty seat.

*

I'll say it though. Lex was a real bitch. She was. From first grade until the day her parents died she was, and she stayed that way until we all graduated and failed at disappearing into the world.

In fifth grade I saw her throw a kid's iPod from a moving bus, and I could feel it, freshman year, when she kicked Cara square in the back. She was unpopular as punk and could break you down with a breath. She was always one foot taller than me.

Her mother modeled in ads for her father's dealership. Golden hair, miles of leg. Tess was her name, the closest thing Deliver had to a bombshell. It took too long for them to clear the billboards.

After three weeks of watching that empty seat, Lex returned with hair much shorter and newly maroon, and no one spoke up anymore when she acted awful. Nobody could stop looking at her.

I still wonder how it feels to have eyes sticking all over your skin.

When Lex caught someone staring, she'd buck, make you flinch, truly scare you. People wondered about her. They really did. Every siren in Deliver we heard, we thought of her.

She bought a yellow Mustang that June and didn't even have her license.

That spring, when she'd pull your chair out and yell *Nerd!* and nobody would chant with her like they were supposed to—but they never told her off either. You'd just sit down on the ground and take it. When she made jokes comparing your hairdo to a sandstorm or stale pasta, you just listened, you just nodded. When she put her hand up in History class to ask, *Why don't we just round up every Muslim and put them on an island?* there wasn't any laughter, and no one called her on her shit. Holding it in is what we learned to do, that and pretend. Like we didn't hear. Like we didn't see.

Senior year, Lex's hair only came to her ears. Plus the color was always new—orange, black, blue. We pretended not to notice, which seemed like a favor to her. But it was only for ourselves. For our comfort.

We both got Best Car that year. My busted Buick Century won out of irony, with a hundred band stickers and little four-leaf clovers stuck all over it. I used to pile in seven misfit friends and spin laps around Deliver, throwing selfish insults at the locals we'd soon be—*Marry me, dumbass! Have you heard the bad news?* My pale hair sometimes sucked out the open window and flapped like wedding streamers.

They announced the superlatives over the loudspeaker during homeroom, our names coming one right after the other, and Lex glared at me like, *How dare you?* One other kid won too, some dick I don't remember with a bright S-10 he flew double confederate flags from.

The three of us had to gather together with our cars for the yearbook picture. I was late that morning, speeding through the parking lot toward her Mustang and the truck, and someone with our school's only SLR on a tripod. I made a big show of circling them twice, revving my shit engine in mock pride. Avenged Sevenfold blared from the one working speaker. My fingers frozen in the morning cold, the windows all down.

It's sad how truly proud it turns out I was.

There were still six months till graduation, but it just felt over.

Their shining cars, I nearly hit them as I parked.

"Watch what the fuck you're doing," Lex said. She had another new haircut—silver, gelled, and spiking out in all directions.

"Would it be funny if I laid across the hood all sexy?" I asked the kid with the camera. I tried to throw my hair back like Paris Hilton. I was on. I really was.

I smirked in Lex's direction, no eye-contact. She raised her fist into the air. I asked coolly if what she thought she was going to do was hit me. The two other kids just watched us, waiting.

The ground shifted as she moved. I couldn't look, but I knew what was coming and ran.

Lex chased me in tight circles around the cars, gaining each lap, closing the narrow gap, her hand groping for the shirt on my back. Four times around we ran before I saw myself from a distant perspective—from the school's security camera, or the sun, or the ghosts in our empty driver's seats—and the humiliation landed. I was winded and stopped and turned and faced her. Our white breath blended. She grinned and tightened and pulled back her arm. I would've let her fist break me if she would have let it go. I would have.

In the photo, she reaches for my curls.

Winter Break

I come home late from a townie party tipsy. The tree tilts
forward forty degrees, suggesting south wind gusts in through
the wall. Upstairs, Mom sleeps sprawled atop the comforter.
With an iPhone for light, collecting wine glasses is not easy, not
unlike an egg-hunt on Easter—I check the windowsill, couch
cushion, toilet tank, sink. Outside, they line the fence, where
her Bichon eats the ivy he'll later vomit into a stocking.

Morning, we open presents and sweat. A card with
nineteen bucks, all in ones, her idea of a gag. Southern
Pennsylvania's heated seventy degrees, and instead of her ex-
boyfriend—at whom yesterday I spat, puffing out my chest to
back him down the stoop, my shaking hand against his Jesus
piece—our subject is weather. "Warmest winter yet," we say.

Mom feeds my hangover hashbrowns spilled from a
bag. She watches her plate, takes cotton-candy drags from a
vape-pen. Before she walks to her Exxon shift, where a wobbly
light will make it hard to see each twenty's watermark, I kiss the
crown of her head, those skeletal roots. My name will echo
through the house when she's home.

I pack his stuff haphazardly, heft it out to the shed. The
soft ground underfoot. The guilty birds crowd their feeder.

Dog shit spots the yard like mines. In a blue camp chair I sit
and wait, and with each hour late choose one item to break.
Snap Kid Rock CDs. Tear the sleeves from size-small Tapout
tees. Leather jacket in the trash. There's no law. All
provocation. I text his cell, want it finished. Want a mess. Want
everything I haven't given, every gift we haven't gotten, to be
punched wildly into his person, this body who creeps her
property. Instead, by sundown, I'm in my Jeep,
honking *sorry* at the dog with his mouth full of leaves.

New Year's Eve, I grip a little sophomore by his jacket
collar. Our faces red and thieving. I hold him up to the light
like a fifty.

Glue

The new cemetery was our only and empty. That March, even before the abandoned farmhouse off Route 31 got demolished and dragged away in pieces, *The Weekly Tattle* reported the land had been bought by a Life Celebration corporation— Milton, Kentucky, population 121, would soon have our own graveyard.

Clean red tractors tilled that acre all spring, and in May men rolled out sod like green carpet. For a solid month, "No Trespassing" signs were the only things put in the earth. When Mrs. Allen, the owner, broke ground on the last day of eighth grade, shaking hands for a photo shoot, her gleaming shovel struck upon the bones of a long dead dog.

"Lousy omen," Meredith said to me. She was sharp. The kind of girl who wore a bookbag high on her back, like a packed parachute. She didn't like the idea of one day burying her parents here. Preferable to bury them out on the beautiful flat prairie, where our school and the Walmart were located, not in this rocky river-valley village, where the wind was so loud and everything green kept wet forever. "Shouldn't nobody put nobody in this ground," she said.

I nodded, reached for her hand, and found it gluey. She'd done an Elmer, still drying. I pulled and the skin on our palms stretched together.

While they waited for the sod to take, Mrs. Allen and her husband celebrated their first entrepreneurial endeavor with a big whoop cruise to Aruba. So all June long Meredith and I spent our days lying in their grass, ears to what was now their ground, listening for our own clues. As a boy, I'd dug through the abandoned barn many times, made stories about the family who'd lived there, had their old rotary phone in my room. It was hard to ask my parents anything about the past without picking at the scabs of their wounded marriage. No one had left anyone yet, but it was all they ever yelled about. I stayed away from the house a lot that summer.

Instead I lay with Meredith, alone in the new cemetery, the ocean of lawn sprawling around us. We stretched out like dogs, palms open, and whoever's turn it was to bring the glue deposited a drop on each finger of the other's hand. You used your thumb to rub it in. With the direct heat of that southern sun, the glue dried almost immediately. Then we took turns peeling each other. It felt like magic, like unwrapping a gift. To feel your skin breathe as that milky sheen teased away.

We didn't do much else beside listen to the breeze in the trees and talk. Theories abounded about the people who owned the land before. It was something in the vibration of the ground, Meredith said, that assured her they kept horses. She was so much smarter than me. She used the word "America" a lot, and in ways I couldn't grasp. "America is wrong," she always concluded. "Even as Americans we're Unamericans."

I nodded along, pretending, angling my body in the grass for a view down her shirt. If I ever asked her what she meant by anything, she'd sigh and say, "Look it up."

If you were able to peel carefully and completely an entire finger's worth of glue, you won—which means you got to kiss the other person wherever you pleased. I lived with a pitiful nail-biting habit, but that summer became my first brush with self-control. The nail on my middle finger grew long and strong and never touched my mouth. Still, no matter how gingerly I worked my nail around the edges of Meredith's palm, no matter how steadily I pulled, her gluey peel always split. Wasn't the worst outcome. The longer it took to remove her Elmer's, the longer I got to hold her hand.

"I bet this place was full of murderers," Meredith said once, her blonde hair spread across the grass. An ant crawled around her collarbone—even the sight of it made me flinch—but she didn't care.

"That's a fun word to say," I said. "Murderers."

"Murderers."

The ant disappeared into her cleavage. "Murderers," I repeated, and we traded the word back and forth until it decayed into a jumble of R sounds and laughter.

At our game, Meredith was a pro. She reached for my hand, quickly peeling a piece that started at my pointer finger and wrapped entirely to my pinky. Her victories—even this grand-slam—always ended in a kiss to my forehead. She had an eighteen-year-old boyfriend who'd been deployed to Iraq back in February. We never discussed Alex, but I was about the only person who knew of their relationship. He had a full beard and wrote her short but heartfelt letters in all capitals. Meredith claimed she could smell his sweat on the paper.

His was one of the first bodies put in our cemetery. After July Fourth, when the sod had been determined healthy and rooted, the ground steadily began to fill with bones, and our afternoons ended, our stupid game declared a tie.

But sometimes, in August, whenever I spotted a creeping line of cars pass my house, those tiny American flags sticking up from windshields like ears, I'd follow on my scooter. Under the hot sun, I'd spy on the funeral, sucking at the sweat gathering on my upper lip's peach fuzz. It wasn't that I enjoyed the tears, the predictable ceremony, or even the preacher's nonsense words. It was the way, once all was said and done—everyone gone back to someone's house for sandwiches and stories—the way the men, in their denim suspenders, would cover the upturned dirt by unrolling, so gently, a square of perfect grass. The way that, if it weren't for the headstone, you wouldn't know anyone had ever been there at all.

"Divebombing" is This Thing I Do With Camera One-Twelve on Forney Towers Where I Focus on the Wide Horizon of Trees and Electric Windmills and Then Begin a Slow Simulated Suicide by Zooming-in and Arcing the Angle Patiently Downward Until Rooftops, then Windows, Doors, Bushes, a Street, and a Sidewalk Pass Overhead, and Finally the 10x Digital Zoom Fuzzes Everything About a Slab of Concrete Forty Stories Down

My boss pronounces "corgi" with a soft "g." My boss knows the city's every intersection and pothole. He prefers the term "criminal" over "crook" and thinks the Safety Coalition has an image problem. My boss makes awkward, unwarranted admissions about his personal life. He's fifty-four but comes off ageless, immortal, like he came out of an ancient magic lamp.

My boss talks to the monitors, has a name for every camera, and it sounds like some are named the same as his cats. He says things like, "You're swimming in the biggest river in Africa—Denial—It's an old AA thing." My boss laughs mostly through his nose. My boss zooms in on citizen's faces and calls each one by name. Sometimes it's like he's looking for his son.

My boss jogs up the hill on Chesapeake. He stresses we're instrumental in arrests. Day One my boss showed me a video he keeps saved on the desktop of a wild deer prancing through King Square and I asked how that could happen. My boss says things like, "I'll tell you this: It's the wild west we're watching."

My boss gets coffee with the cops. My boss hopes I'm the next him. My boss says things like, "having a domestic." He's been here since they built Linear park, manned the cameras since the grant in '02, and its hard to tell, but I'd guess its five years he's been divorced.

He's not easy to read. My boss wears glasses with one temple missing, a faint almost-moustache, and he's bald. My boss never cleans the Keurig. My boss lives on Locust near Missen

Park and files complaints about the congregants of O'Malley's Pub. He recites city ordinance codes like an epic poem.

My boss is the only full-time employee at the Coalition. He wonders what the world could be doing if it tried harder. My boss says things like, "I'll tell you this: my counselor's going to need counseling when she's finished with me." My boss loves the parade. He bought a police scanner for his bedroom.

My boss reminds me of my firefighter father: good at something no one likes to think about. My boss hasn't ordered me a Safety Coalition polo yet because, I think, he's waiting me out, to see if I quit from the boredom or the horror of seeing someone shot. My boss says to call him anytime I have a problem except for Thursday nights from 20:00 to 20:30 due to the new *Big Bang Theory*.

My boss doesn't know that when I'm on overnights I blast rap music through the computer speakers. He doesn't know I work out and clip my toenails and take my shirt off if I'm bored and sometimes turn all eighteen monitors to camera one-twelve and divebomb.

My boss calls me at 5:00 AM to repeat what I just heard over the scanner: the police believe the suspect in last week's smash and grab at the Stop & Go was loitering near the corner of Vine and Forney between 18:00 and 18:30 last night. I can do the review myself but my boss tells me to bring up playback for cameras one hundred, thirty-three, and one-twelve. He'll be there in ten.

In the early morning, my boss and I watch recorded footage at 8x speed and it's disorienting and shows us nothing of a suspect with ponytail and a red jersey. My boss says our best bet is camera one-twelve. While I bring up the feed and wonder where I'll find my next job, my boss reminds me of all you can see from the top of Forney Towers: half the city, hawks, the wildflower preserve, windmills on Turkey Hill, seagulls somehow, and almost the Susquehanna River. My boss's jaw hangs open as I play for us nineteen minutes of divebombs. He waits it out in silence. "I'll tell you this," my boss says, "that's beautiful."

Mannequins

And when we leave the Galleria, we have each other and a mannequin arm. And the eight of us bottom out my dad's Buick Regal on every speed bump. And Biggie's on the Zune, blasting from one working speaker. And Kole bounces our stolen limb out the window. And that plastic arm's even paler than ours, but at least it has rhythm. At least we know the words to the one part, about where to put our hands if we're careless. So the arm is in the air. And in eight months we graduate and some of us are jailed and some of us die quickly in another country and some of us take much longer. And the cold is bitter and blowing, but we have body heat. And the red light traffic's backed up so bad we're stuck in the middle of an intersection. And a chorus of car horns comes at us from all directions. And we crank the stereo until the song crumbles, and despite everything our arm waves and chops and bobs. And we're in shambles from laughter, can't even compose a sentence. And the trio in the middle bench screams to our audience, "Go home, tell the motherfuckers what you love about us!"

*

We wanted to be talked about. To be the subjects of gossip, and songs, and long auditorium lectures. We wanted the very mention of our names to bring laughter. Our life was a stick-up, and we needed your attention, all of it, put it in the bag.

And Kole honks the horn because the cars won't go. And Jayson beats the ceiling for bass. And I slap the rearview mirror off the windshield, because nothing behind us matters. And now the song is Snoop Dogg. And someone in the back opens a confetti bomb he stole from the party store.

We were the party store, always open. Everything in our lives was a gift, and still, we stole. At Walmart, we emptied diaper boxes in the bathroom, filled them with Miley CDs, and sold them all to FYE for gas money. Spent that expensive fuel just cruising, stupid, pulling up to your front door and laying on the horn. We came home after dawn only to watch our fathers wake in a dark daze, shuffle to the truck, and start the motor of the future. The future looked like pawning, one after another, every gift we'd ever been given, every moment we'd stolen.

And the light's still red. And the Zune, on shuffle, switches to something acoustic, but everyone's like, no, no, no. And, no, we don't see a grown man on a boy's bike, pedaling along the shoulder, wearing an Olive Garden polo, with no coat, sweating through the cold.

Our theory was that we could collect enough of the heaviest kind of laughter and finally stop time.

And the traffic is stuck still. And the emo ballad croons, *When you're twenty-six, will you still be in the pit with the kids?* And I hit a button and the song is Slayer. And I rip the arm out of Kole's hands, crank my window, punch the thing out there and it slams the coatless man on the Huffy, sends him off the stony shoulder, down the embankment, disappeared.

We want so bad to laugh. But everyone is stunned silent. And I let the arm drop from my hand down to the road. And now, now, now the light goes green. And the traffic starts to shift. And go, go, go, we're all screaming. But Kole won't touch the gas pedal. And we know why, but still we yell why, why, why, until the man rises up from the side of the road like the undead, bleeding from an eyebrow, old snow in his beard. And that's when he grabs our arm from the gravel. And he holds it by the wrist with both of his fists. And he raises it like a scythe. And we don't close our eyes. And the music turns to blues, a song dad uploaded to my Zune on Christmas Eve. *Judge and jury, please just stop me.* I've never heard it before or again and the arm comes down, shoulder first—DUNT—

against the windshield—*Please just stop me*—and he raises it back up—DUNT—hammers it again—*Please*—and every time it comes down, it comes down heavier—DUNT—and we see his lips moving as the glass begins to split.

And still we pretend we don't know what he's telling us.

Out, Out

And then we were in fall and took a bus to your mother's house (and I'd always assumed she was dead, the way you spoke of home in the past tense). We were way out in Okeechobee, lugging with us that street sign I helped you steal because it said her name, *JODI St.*

Saint Jodi, you said.

On the long ride out we shared our daily bottle of Dayquil, and when the bus stopped we waded back into the heavy heat, those weird water turkeys flying over from Nubbins Slough, cawing at each other in long, awful creaks. Anhinga, you told me, it's Brazilian for devil-bird. Hunts its prey entirely underwater, head and all. I took your hand. It sneaks up on fish. It moves like a snake.

We staggered around that maze of neighborhood looking for a doublewide with a pebble yard. You said hers would be the only ornamentless property in the complex. And, like everything you ever said, that was true—no crystal balls, no woodcuts of boys pissing on the house, not a single pink flamingo—and when we got there you told me to hang out out here, and even though I was parched as fuck and had to piss and wanted to see if St. Jodi's eyes switched colors the way, in sunlight, yours did, I obeyed and crouched beside the dying palm tree. How hard is it to let a palm live? It stood crooked, brown leaves limping down around me, looking like your dreads before we lopped them off and wove each one through the shelter's chain-link fence—our first and best and final act of public art.

Jodi spoke to you through the screen-door, saying, It's not my birthday, she said. It's not my fucking birthday. And I made myself as small as possible. And: Who's that, she asked. And: Nobody, you said. And: There's someone on my property, I'm calling the cops.

And I stood and turned and waved to you both.

You didn't wave back. She said, Who is that?

And I kept just waving. And you said, Nobody. I don't know who that is.

She did not believe you, but I did. You two continued to argue as I wandered the complex, lost for the exit. That's not even how you spell my name, I heard her say.

I was desperate for a CVS, but instead found one of those birds—long neck bent like a spring, beak like a spear, caw like a motor that won't turn over—wading in somebody's blue blow-up pool. It cried out in that foul voice as if for another, but above us both the sky was bare.

*

And now it's summer. I'm back at the Lauderdale shelter. They don't let me eat without lending a hand. I do eggs in a wok. I add milk the way you loved. Remember how you'd plead with the staff to add a cup? How come you never taught me to ask for what I wanted?

I haven't gotten all the way clean yet, but I haven't quit the job. I lead Friday yoga. I lean heavy on corpse pose, where sometimes I can't get empty, and I see you two there on the stoop, how she starts to fix the collar of your dirty polo. Saint Jodi pats your shoulders. The more she touches you, the clearer her vision, the stiller her hands, the pills work again, you never even stole them. She pulls a piece of gum from the pocket of her housedress. Places it on your tongue like a Jesus wafer. She hands you the home phone and says, Please speak to your grandmother. And: Don't worry, she doesn't remember anything. Just tell her you love her.

Acknowledgements

First I want to thank my family for supporting me endlessly—Erin for being my motivator and first reader, Mom for being my inspiration, Dad for being my rock, Jay and Pat for being my champions. These stories would not exist without so many people, but certainly not without the GOF, whose antics, escapades, fears, bliss, and laughter are the seed, root, and fruit of so many of these stories. I also want to thank Barbara Lomenzo and Cassie Ney for fostering my writing in its earliest stages; Eliot White (and the whole CWG) for showing me that writing does not exist without community; anyone who bought that weird stapled chapbook I made at the end of college because I had over a hundred dollars left on my MU printing account and because I was stupid; James Figy, Dennis Herbert, Lissa Horneber, Pete Stevens, Michael Torres, and everyone in Mankato who made me a better writer; Elle Nash and Bud Smith for swapping work and teaching me to follow my gut (not my brain); the entire Split Lip FAM for the constant support; anyone who ever let me interview them about writing; and finally, Petey.

I also want to thank the editors of the following publications for giving these stories their first leap into the world. Special thanks to edits and suggestions from Teege Braune, Matty Byloos, Maureen Langloss, Alex McElroy, Amanda Miska, Kimberly Ann Southwick, and Erin Stalcup.

"Stay, Go" was published in *Gulf Coast*

"Hiccups Forever" was published in *Timber*

"K," was published in *Waxwing* (and a finalist for the 2017 Best of the Net)

"Whatever's the Worst that Could Happen We Want" was published in *NANO Fiction*

"Late-Teens on Trash Night" was published in *Fanzine*

"Models" was published in *Nailed Magazine*

"Winter Break" was published in *No Tokens*

"Glue" was published in *Gigantic Sequins*

"Divebombing . . . " was published in *Knee Jerk Magazine*

"Mannequins" was published in *Split Lip Magazine*

"Out, Out" was published in *Burrow Press*

NOW AVAILABLE FROM

Hungry People
by Tasha Coryell

Felt in the Jaw
by Kristen N. Arnett

I Am the Oil of the Engine of the World
by Jared Yates Sexton

I Once Met You But You Were Dead
by SJ Sindu

Because I Wanted to Write You a Pop Song
by Kara Vernor

For more info about the press and our titles, please visit:

WEBSITE: www.splitlippress.com
TWITTER/INSTAGRAM: @splitlippress

Printed in Great Britain
by Amazon

55858640R00038